THE SLEEPWALKERS

VIVIANE SCHWARZ

WALKER

This is a work of fiction. Names, characters, places and incidents are either the product of the author's imagination or, if real, are used fictitiously. All statements, activities, stunts, descriptions, information and material of any other kind contained herein are included for entertainment purposes only and should not be relied on for accuracy or replicated as they may result in injury.

First published 2013 by Walker Books Ltd
87 Vauxhall Walk, London SE11 5HJ

2 4 6 8 10 9 7 5 3 1

This book has been typeset in WBVschwarz

Printed in China

British Library Cataloguing in Publication Data:
a catalogue record for this book is available from the British Library

ISBN 978-1-4063-2359-7

www.walker.co.uk

DO YOU HAVE A BAD DREAM
THAT WILL NOT GO AWAY?

ARE YOU AFRAID TO SLEEP AT NIGHT?

CALL THE SLEEPWALKERS!

WRITE US A LETTER,
PUT IT UNDER YOUR PILLOW ...

AND WE WILL COME AND SAVE YOU!

HAVE A GOOD NIGHT!

To You

~~Somewhere~~
~~Long ago~~
Before the Morning
There is a Safe House for You
to Shelter in.

When you are afraid
To fall asleep
When all your dreams
Are Nightmares
Write us a letter
Put it under your pillow
We will rescue you.

Friend

FRIEND friend

It's bedtime, Paula!

I'm just writing a letter, Mum!

Hello.
Please help.
Every night I have
a dream of
TOO MANY MICE.
I am afraid to go
to sleep

Ready!

Did you write your letter?
Yes.
Is it for Dad?
No.

Do you want to go and post it together tomorrow?
I already posted it.

Did you? Well. Now, sleep tight, Paula bean, and you'll be taller in the morning.
CLICK

Goodnight.
Goodnight.

Oh.

CHEESE!
It's that dream again.

Everything is made of cheese.

Hello?

I'm all alone ... and it's that dream... But I asked for help...
SQUEE
SQUEE
FONDUE RIVER
CAMEMBERT

SQUEE
SQUEE
SQUEE
SQUEE
SQUEE
SQUEE
No! Not again!

SQUEE
SQUEE
SQUEE
SQUEE
SQUEE
SQUEE
SQUEE
SQUEE
Too many mice!

SQUEE
SQUEE
CHEESE!

SQUEE
Why is no one helping meeeeeee?

SQUEE
Arghhh!
SQUEE
CHEESE!

SQUEE
SQUEE
Woof! Woof! Woof!
SQUEE

SQUEE
SQUEE
GRAB

SQUEE
CRUMBLE
SQUEE
SQUEE

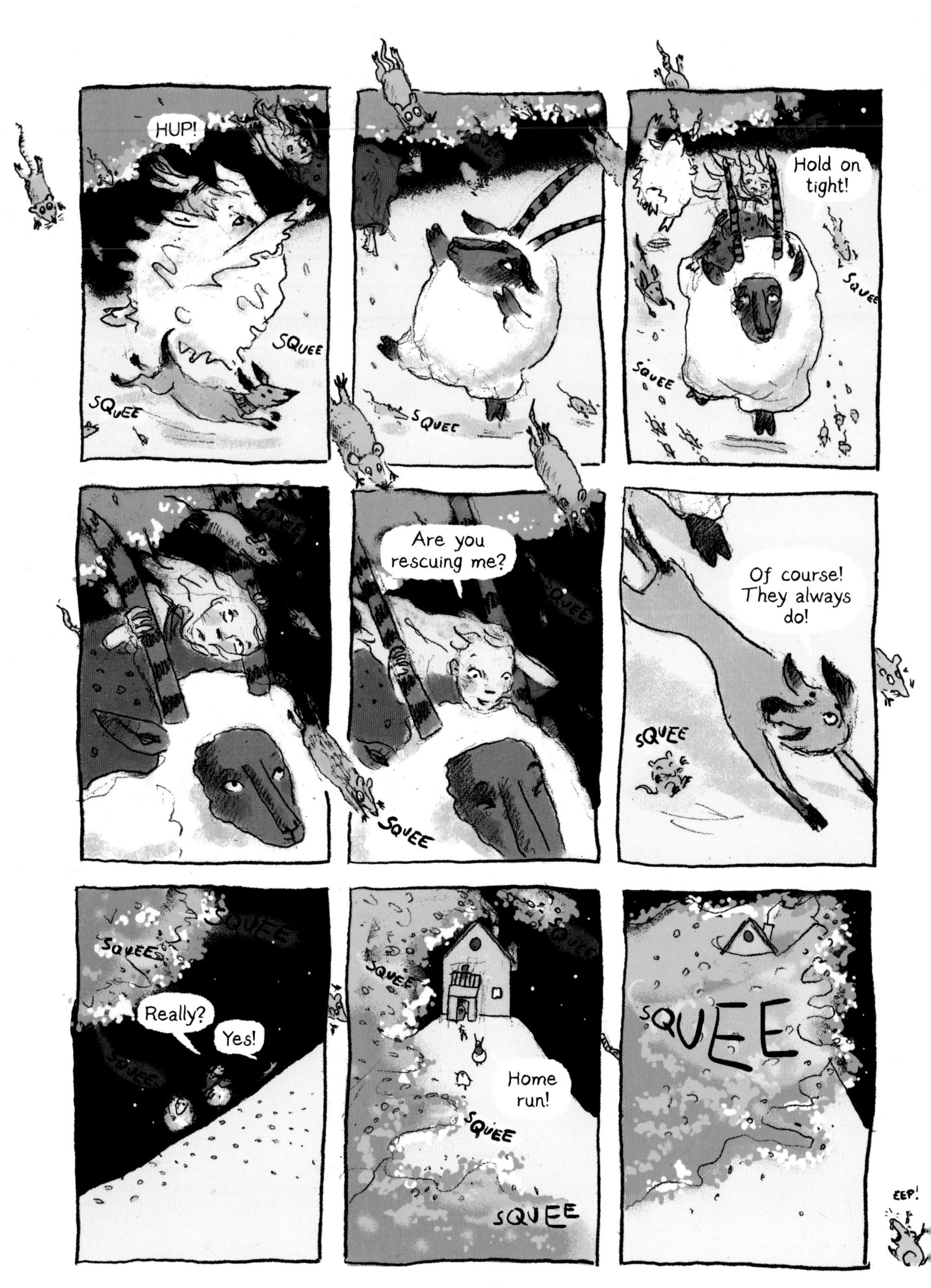
HUP!
SQUEE
SQUEE
SQUEE
Hold on tight!
SQUEE
SQUEE
SQUEE
Are you rescuing me?
SQUEE
Of course! They always do!
SQUEE
SQUEE
Really?
Yes!
SQUEE
Home run!
SQUEE
SQUEE
SQUEE
EEP!

CHEESE!
SQUEEE
CHEESE!
SQUEE
SQUEEE
CHEESE
SQUEE
CHEESE!
SQUEE

SQUEE
SQUEE

Welcome to the Safe House. Would you like a hot drink?

Look! They're eating the moon! But we've escaped!
No problem.

How will I ever get home?

Your bad dream is over. You can go back home any time!
Exactly! Wake up safe and happy!

And you?
We are home already.

Will you save me again tomorrow?

No problem.
Here, take this.
It's a catamaran.

It's inflatable.
Try it.

POP

POP
Wow!

Next time you'll just sail away in this!

It's very portable. Rolls right up.
PFFFFFFFFFFFFF

This way. Happy waking!
Thank you so much!

Bye-bye, Paula!
CLICK
SLUMP
Oof.
GOODBYE
TWEETY
TWEET
TWEET
TWEET
TWEET
TWEET
TWEET
TWEET
TWEETY
TWEET
TWEET
TWEET
TWEET
TWEET
TWEETY
Are you OK?
Yes. Just a bit tired.
TWEET
Well, I think I threw my hip out! Ha! And look ... mouse-bite!
TWEET
Listen...

It always sounds so peaceful out there... I wish I could go see...
You know you can't.

Yeah. You know what would happen ... HA.
Yes ... it's not time yet.

It is time.
SCRITCH
SCRITCH

Really?
Already?

Yes. We are getting old. It's time.

We are almost ready. There is only one last thing we need. Buddy...
Yup.

See ... here. You will find it here. An old thing. A safe thing.
Got it!

You alone can fetch it. Bring it here.

We will wait.

SALE

SALE

Nice doggy.
SALE

Are you hungry?
SALE

Not?
SALE

You look like you want something.

I used to have a dog.
She used to play with shoes.

SALE

So what do you want? Take your pick.
No one's buying anyway.

What? You want that?
SALE

My old bedspread...? It's kind of coming apart now.

Like there...
It's very old.
My great-great-grandma made it.

I used to wrap up in it and be a bear, and then fight with Pip.
She'd try and skin me. Grrr.

Pip was my dog. When I was a boy.
If I had a dog now, I would let him sleep on the blanket.

You want that old rag, eh? Do you? Do you?
Rrrr.

Whoa!

SALE

SALE

GOODBYE

Hey! Wake up! I got it!

Oh ... very good...
What? What?

This is the one. Excellent material. Good man, Buddy. This blanket has great spirit.
That looks quite powerful!
It smells nice, too. Like popcorn.

We should raise the hero as soon as possible.
Before breakfast?

Do we have time before the nightmare manifests?
Yes.
I'll boil the kettle.

We can have tea later. This is momentous!
I know it is! So?

There. Now we are ready. Take your places, please.
Let's begin.
Right.

Baa.
Baa.
Baa.

Baa.
Baa.
Baa.

Baa.
Baa.
Baa.

Zip!
Zap!

What?
It is done.
"Zip zap"?

Welcome to the Safe House.
Do not worry. All is well.
Welcome, Bonifacius.

"Bonifacius"?
It's a good name.
He's my apprentice, right?
Come on downstairs...

I don't understand. My head hurts.
That's probably normal.

I have ... a ... head?
You were a blanket for a hundred years. It will take some time to get used to being a bear.

A hundred years? What was I before?
Cup of tea?
I was tea?

You were nothing. But while you were a blanket, you became a bit of a bear. And now you are a bear all through. Have some tea.

Now, let me explain.

I am a bear...
I always say, a cup of tea will sort out most confusions.

This is the Safe House. It can withstand the strongest nightmares, and it travels between them to take the Sleepwalkers wherever we are needed.

Needed?

Yes, we help defeat the horrors. There are many horrors... For every thought, there is a fear, and for every fear, there is a dream...

Most dreams are good, mind, or else how would anyone get anywhere in life? But some become nightmares and dreamers can get stuck in them.

Hey Buddy! This is Bonifacius.
Five ... four ...
Woof! Woof! Woof!

Approaching target.
You're doing well.

AAAAAAAAAAH!!!
This way.

Whoa!

Help!
Hi Bonno! Pleased to meet you.
... three ... two ...

... one...

Target!

SNAP

Um ... what's that big thing down there?
Yay!
Hey, wow! It's like flying!
No.
AAAAAAAAAAAAAH!
No ground?
Technically there is no ground. So no problem.
AAAAAAAAAAAAAAAAHHHH!!!
But ... AAAAAH!!!
We've got you!
I got ... hang on.
I got you.
It's damp.
Must be a rain cloud.
I suggest we link hands.
Good idea! Here...
FOOMPH
FOOMPH
FOOMPH
FOOMPH
FOOMPH
Oh ... it's...
It's the ground!!!

Yay!
Arh! What is this? I'm buzzing!!!
BZZT
BZZT
Dream energy!
BZZT

Checking dream pressure. It's ... up!
Giddy-up!
I believe this has ceased to be a nightmare.

Wahey!

PLOP
Ah.

Look out!

This is awesome!
Wargh!
ZAP!
Let's retreat to the house.

This is perfectly normal.
ZAP!

ZAP!
There must be a horror near by.

EEEEEEEEEEEEEE
A prehistoric plane! I did **not** expect that.
EEEEE
Charge!

GULP!
Change of plan. Let's infiltrate the enemy.
WHOOSH
PFFF
CHUGG
CHUGG
CHUGG
Sniff.
HONK
TWEET
COO
Wrong way!
This sure is one hungry plane!
KWA!
NOM
NOM
NOM
CROSS-SECTION

How interesting!
Passengers!
SQUAA
SQUAWK
CHIRP
CHEE
CHIRP
TWEET
EEEK
TWEET
TWOODLE
TWEET
Woo Hoo

Whoa.
SQUEE
This is scary now!
SQUAWK
CHOMP!
GRARGH
New arrivals!

This is horrible. I don't want any more dinosaurs.
SQUA
ROAR
TWEET

AAAH! WE ARE CRASHING! AAAAH!

SQUEE
AAAAAH!
TWEET

I'm going to investigate.

KWAA
TWEET

SQUAWK
TWOO

BOINK

BUMPH

Now ... how does this work?
TAP
TAP
TAP

Up! Up!
Yes, yes...

Good work! Is it under control?
Aye aye!

Look, it's quite easy. This one makes it go up and down, and this makes it go faster...
Let me try!

I am the prince of all pilots!

That was excellent!
Can I keep it?

Here you go, sir. Enjoy your flight, madam.
RAAA

So we can leave now?
Sure! I just found some parachutes.

Going right up to drop you off!

Right! GO! GO! GO!
EEEEEE

EEEEEEE

EEEEEEE

How did it go?
He did very well.

Congratulations on your first mission. Rest up now. We'll see you tomorrow.
Uh ... thanks.

Wasn't that fun?
Fun? No. No, it wasn't fun.

No? But ... we got to parachute down from a giant metal bird.
And the boy was really happy and ...

... you did GREAT!
Oh well. Is there food here?

Hey! Yeah! You got hands! Open the fridge! Open the fridge!
Right.

Hey! This is brilliant. Hey, let's try to eat it all before you go to your room.

I have a room?

Sure! Didn't they show you?
No.

I'll show you later.

THE SAFE HOUSE

COMPLETELY DREAM-PROOF AND SELF-NAVIGATING

Emergency exit through folly

← The Library contains such works as "Tentacle Wrestling for Dummies" and "The Secrets of the Universe" (expanding edition).

Shower room

Master Bedroom

Guest Room

BALCONY

UPSTAIRS

The attic houses the ancient armoury.

Central Vent

ATTIC

The office desk contains 6 kinds of ink.

OUT

DOWNSTAIRS

The thinking chair

GARAGE

The Kitchen is always well stocked.

← Loo

Deliveries are sorted here.

IN

The basement holds the specimen collection, the workshop and the creature who grew the house as a shell (see "History of the House", in the library).

The basement creature feeds through the plumbing.

zZZ zzZZ---

Good morning. I trust you slept well?
Don't talk to him before he's had some tea, it's cruel.

SLURP
It seems a little boy is lost in a forest.
A forest? Wonderful! Any wildlife?
Very much so.
Oh my! We must take samples.

RRRUMBLE

The house has landed! A new nightmare is afoot.

What? Another one? Already?

Well ... not quite yet. Dream pressure is still low.

Let's raise another apprentice then!

You can be best friends.
Good plan. Where's Buddy?

Wff!

Aaaaaaah. Good man, Buddy. These are just right.
RRRRR

Watch this. It's a really good trick. Best thing to do with socks...

Like this ... and so...
SLICE
Careful there!

I know what I'm doing.
I know you know what you're doing.

And some stuffing...
SHAVE

It looks flabby. Let's shave off some more...
It's fine.

Is that how they made me?
Pretty much.

I am stuffed with your wool?
Hardly. Then I'd be bald.

There!
Oooh!
Ooooh!

Excuse us for a while.
He looks nice.
I think she's a girl.

BAA
BUMP
BAA
BUMP
BAA
They're doing the dance!

THUNK
Come alive!
BAA
Oh, it's done!

SHUFFLE
Oh oh oh there'll be adventure and a new friend and I wonder where we'll go today oh don't you?

Well ... I hope you like trees.

OH WOW!

I LOVE TREES!

Wonderful! Let's go and explore!
YAY! BRILLIANT!

Apparently there are monsters out there...
OH YEAH! MONSTERS!

They're not taking us.

Come on, then. Let's do some sword training!
Wow!

Wow! Gee! Can I watch?
No.

I bet you'll be AWESOME!

Now let's have some fun!

This is the armoury. Look around! All this will be yours soon.
Really? My goodness.

But first ... I have something to give you.

The Sword of Rin — Warrior Prince and Keeper of the Forgotten Shrine.

Doesn't he want it?
No. He doesn't want it any more.

A long time ago, it was given to me and with it I have cut down many nightmares. Now the time has come to hand it to my successor.

That's you. Take it already.
touch

The Sword of Rin, Slayer of Trouble. And now yours, for a time.
Um ... you sure?

It is yours, don't worry. Try holding it like this.

OW!
OW!
OW!

MMMMM.
Oh, let me see that...

PAF

Sorry sorry sorry sorry sorry sorry.
No, that was quite good — I didn't see it coming at all. We should work with that.

I can't do this. You got the wrong guy. That's someone else's sword. You better go find them...

Ach, well ... I guess you don't actually have to USE it...

Let's just keep it ... yes! There. That's nice.
You like it there?

Oh! Sounds like they're back!
HONK
TOOT
BWAARK

Hey! How'd it go?
MEAOWZ

TWEEE
CHITTER
ROAR
WOO HOO! We brought back SAMPLES!
BWAAA
MOO

FFFT
MOOO
No problem!
Thank you for teaching me to tame the beasts.
RRRR

MWAAA
Goodbye! Thanks for the awesome nightmare!
TWEE
Thank you! Bye-bye!

SNIFF
These beasts are very interesting. I would like to have a closer look at their plumage.

We thought you would.
HONK
SIGH

You OK?

The monkey looks nice.
Hm. She didn't look scared, that's for sure.

I'm scared all the time.

That monkey is made for the job. Why didn't they make me as well as they made her?
Oh, they didn't make you — they just raised you.

Who made me then?
Um ... someone's gran.

Great.

Hi! My name's Amali. How are you guys doing?
Fine.
Hi Amali!

Isn't this great? I had so much fun taming beasts!
Glad to hear it.

Great dream, isn't it? I love it. Everyone's made of HAIR!

Just look at it!
It's amazing!
We went on and on and
on ... there's no end to it.
And anything could be out
there! Anything!
It's brilliant!

Yes ... anything at all...
Shall we wait out there for the next dream? Oh, ho ho, let's!
Nah. The house won't travel if anyone is still awake.
Aww. OK, let's all go and sleep so we'll get there quicker! Come on!
You can have the spare room if you like.
Oh, I'd rather stay with you guys. You've got to tell me how this place works and all.
We can have a sleepover!
I guess so.
Great! Hey, let's open the fridge again!
Goodnight, guys! See you tomorrow!

HOW TO MAKE A SOCK MONKEY
TWO SOCKS
OR MORE
they need not match
WOOL
for sewing
a big blunt needle
Scissors
BUTTONS
stuffing
TOE
HEEL
Flatten the first sock out so the heel is on top
then cut it like this to make legs.
The heel becomes the bottom
sew up the legs but leave a hole for...
STUFFING!
fill the body & legs & sew it shut.
HOW TO SEW:
Always tie the end with a knot
use wool shorter than your arm
stitch AROUND & AROUND
when the wool gets short...
tie a knot & start a new bit.
Take the second sock and cut here...
and cut here.
This will be the snout
Put the snout over the head like a mask
sew the arms...
Stuff the snout & stuff the arms
& sew them all on!
BUTTON EYES
EARS
A TAIL IS NICE

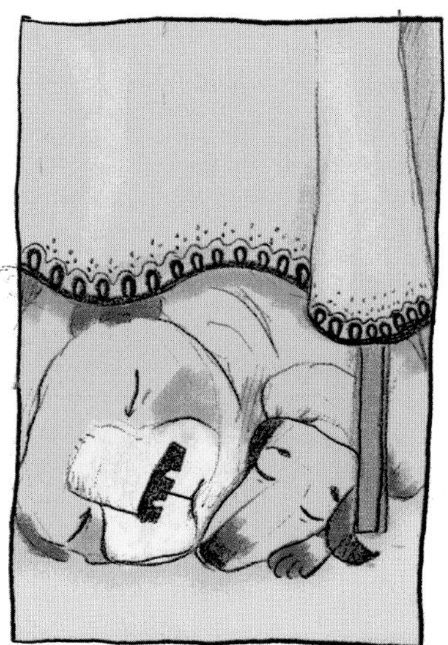

click

Buddy?
What's up?

It's the letter!

What letter?
Th' l'tt'r! Th're's alw's a l'tt'r.

Morning, guys! Hey, what's with the letter?

Is it for us?
It's for the Sleepwalkers.
That's us!

PLEASE HELP ME.
I ALWAYS HAVE THIS DREAM
AND IT WON'T GO AWAY.
I AM SWIMMING IN THE SEA.
IT GOES ON FOREVER.
I SEE AN ISLAND.
THEN I SEE THAT IT'S THE TOP
OF A VERY TALL TOWER
AND I KNOW THE WORLD IS
SUNK
AND I BECOME SINKY.
THEN I SINK DOWN AND THE
WATER IS COLD AND DARK.

I DON'T WANT TO DREAM THAT
ANY MORE. PLEASE MAKE
IT STOP. REGARDS, TIMMY

See you later!

Did they give you that thing? Do you know how it works?
Mm.
WHIRR

One ball points to where the dreamer is. And the other back to the house. And this "whirr" is the dream pressure.
WHIRRRRRR
WHIRRRRRR

There's the tower!
WHIRR

Timmy! HEY! WHERE ARE YOU?
The dream pressure is going up! Swim faster!
WHIRR

OH NO! OH NO!
What?
WHIRR
WHIRR
We are TOO LATE!

He's underwater! NOOOOOOOOO!

It's OK. Looks like he's still asleep.
WHIRRRRRR

I think I should swim to that tower.

We need to do something. The sheep are watching.
Yes they are — and drinking tea.

I have an idea!

Don't worry, this will work!

All right. HEPP!

SPLASH

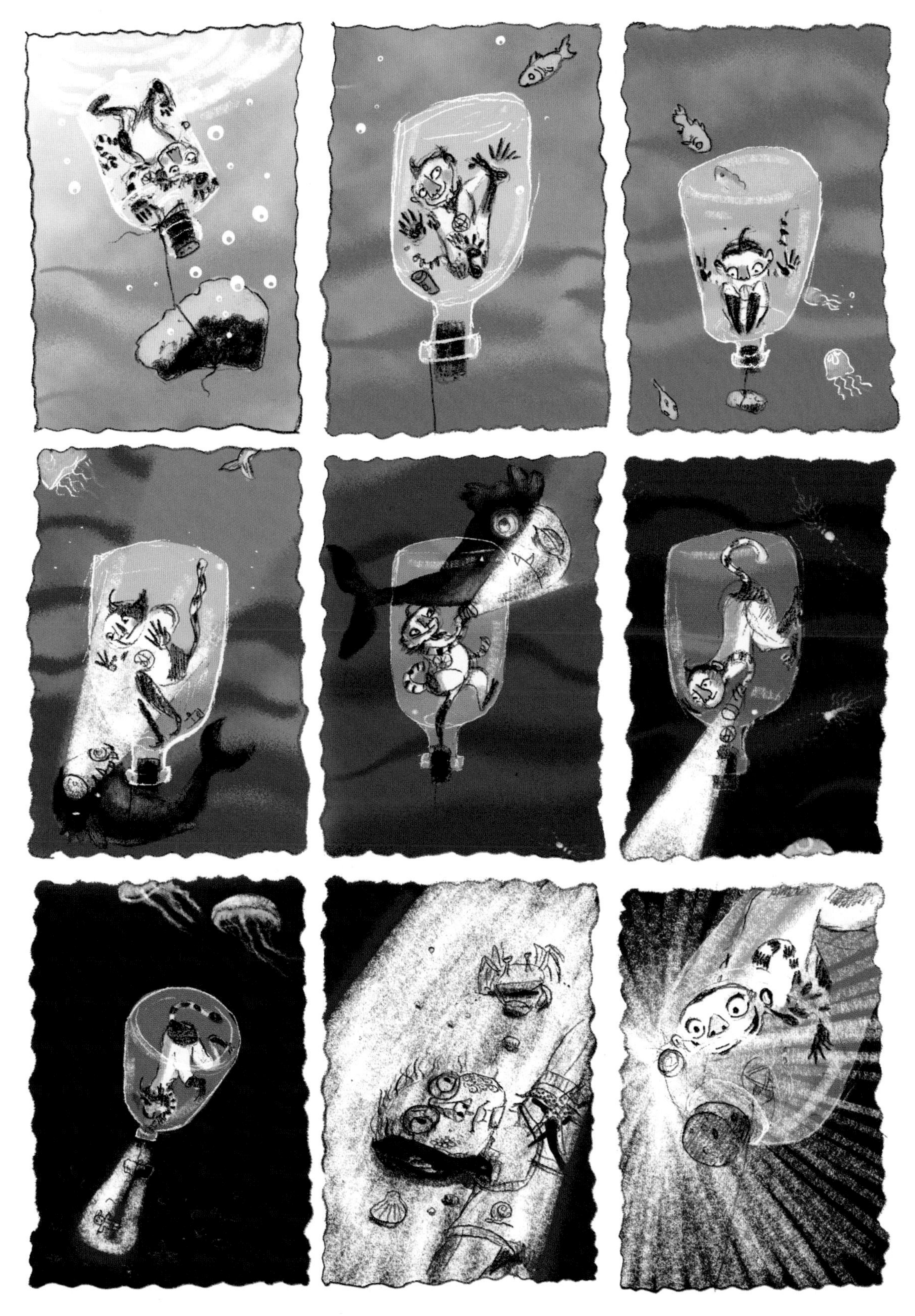

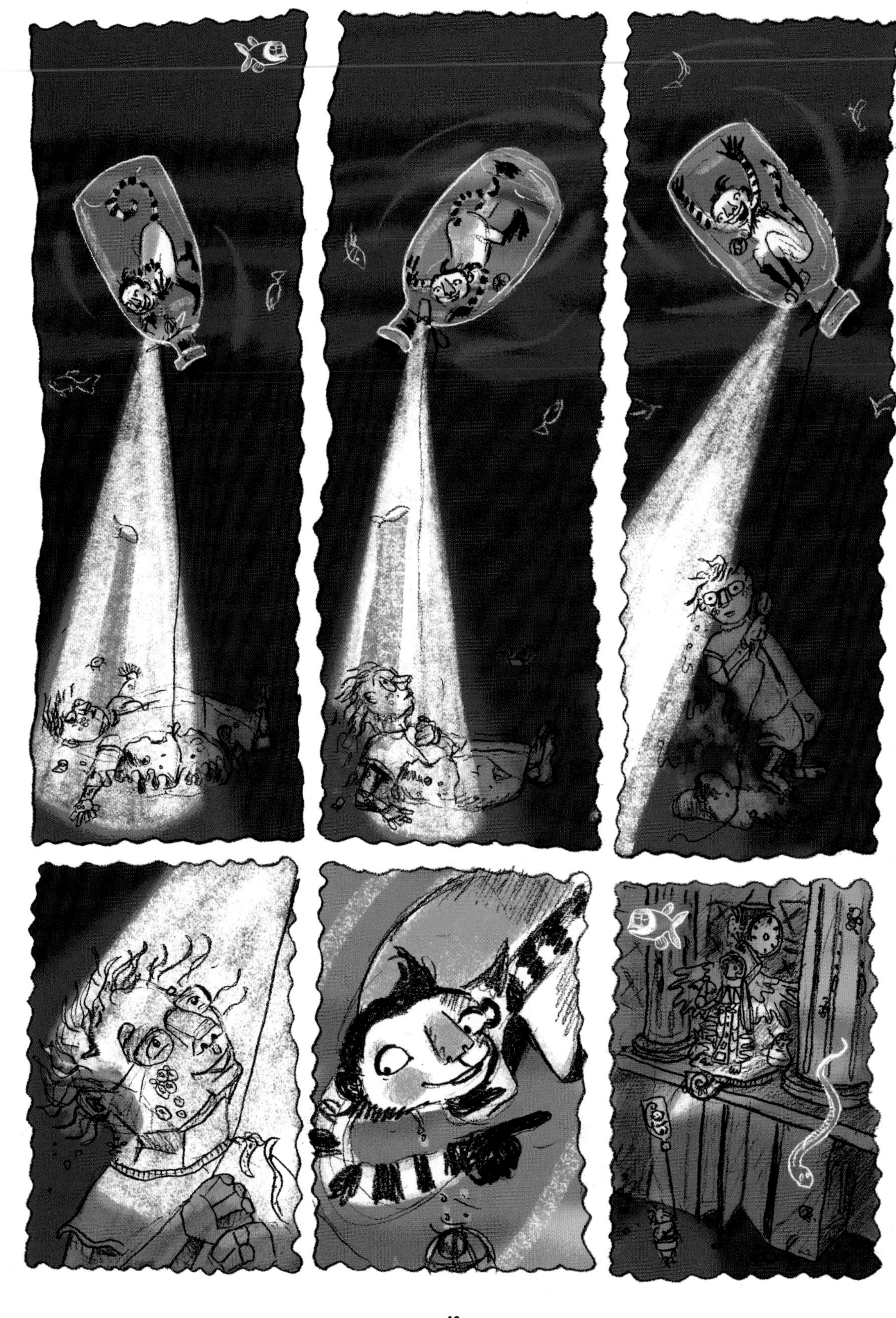

TOYS
BOOKS
PERFUME
FASHION

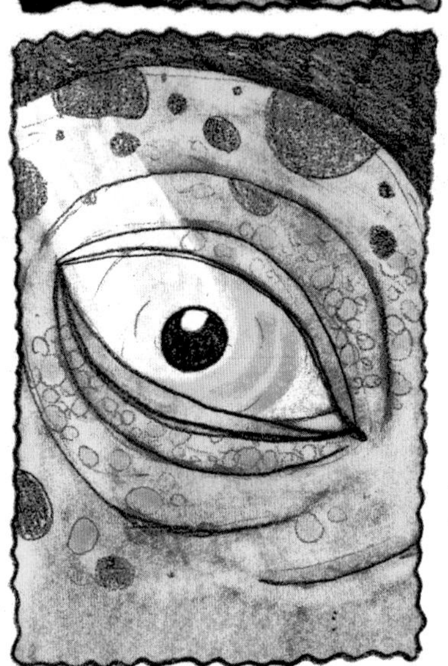

CRASH
CRACK

There they are!

Fetch the plank.
I have the bait.

OPEN YOUR BEAK, YOU...
Woof!
Woof!
Woof!

Anyone for some tasty salad?

I knew you were watching. I wasn't scared.
I was.

Next time I turn to stone I won't worry. Nothing can eat me anyway!
What an amazing animal. This carapace is incredibly tough.
I like it. Can we keep it in the garage?
Great idea!

Your apprentice has proved herself.
Yes. Yes, she has. I guess it's time ... to go home.

Oh, can't I stay a bit longer? I don't have to get up early today. It's Sunday.

Of course. Amali? Will you come with me?

Goodbye, everyone.

He looks sad.
Yeah ... yeah, I think we should...

I am very proud of you. You will do very well.
Thank you!

No problem.

Hang on! Wait! You...

What's up?

I thought you said only you can go through that door?

Only I can come back.

Amazing creature! I believe its shell is completely horror-proof.
Can we convert it into an armoured vehicle? We should ask...

Oh...

Timmy, how about a cup of tea before you leave, hm?

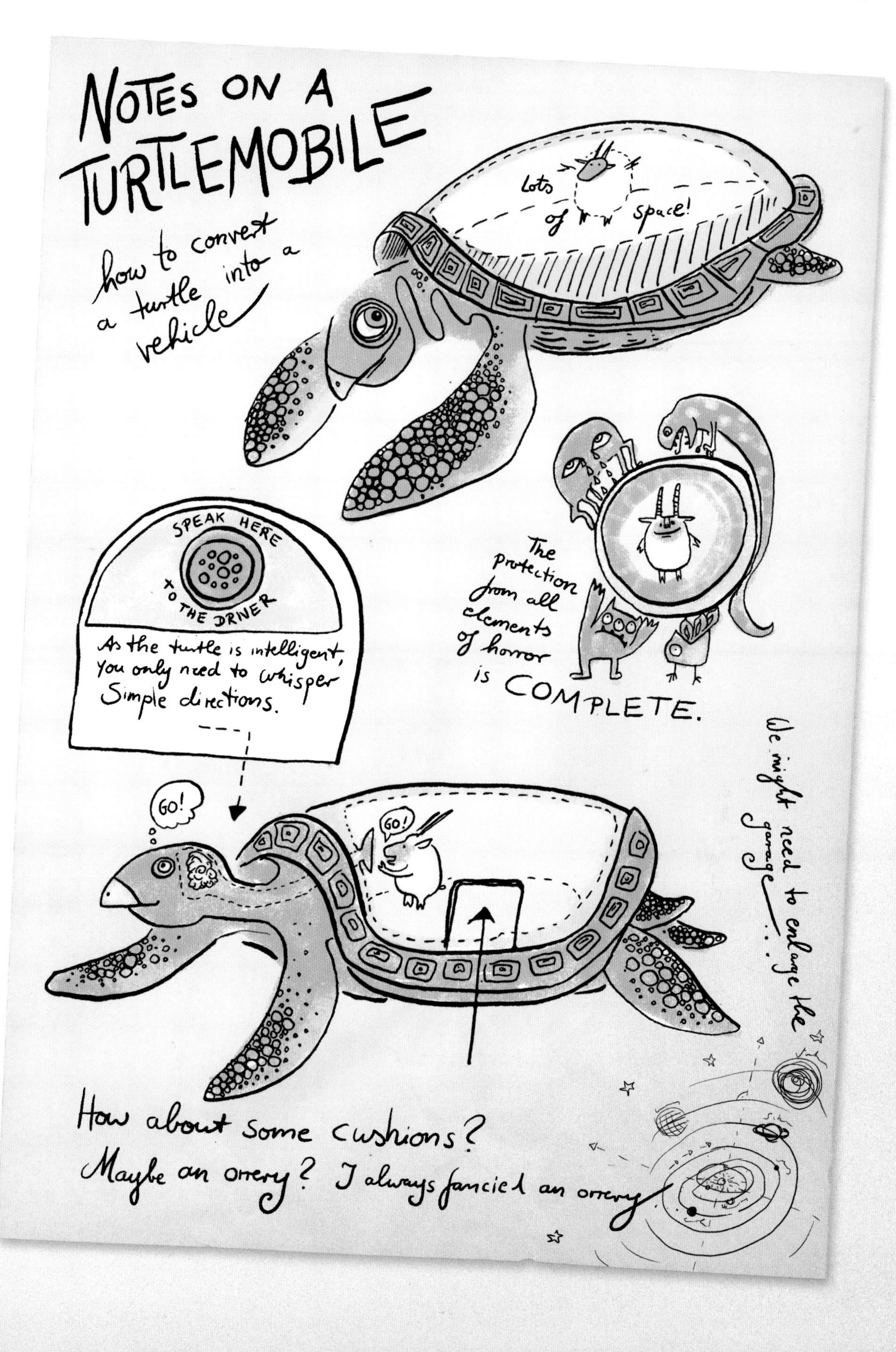
NOTES ON A TURTLEMOBILE
how to convert a turtle into a vehicle
Lots of space!
SPEAK HERE TO THE DRIVER
As the turtle is intelligent, you only need to whisper Simple directions.
The protection from all elements of horror is COMPLETE.
GO!
GO!
We might need to enlarge the garage...
How about some cushions?
Maybe an orrery? I always fancied an orrery!

Bonno?
Yes?
I'm still sad.

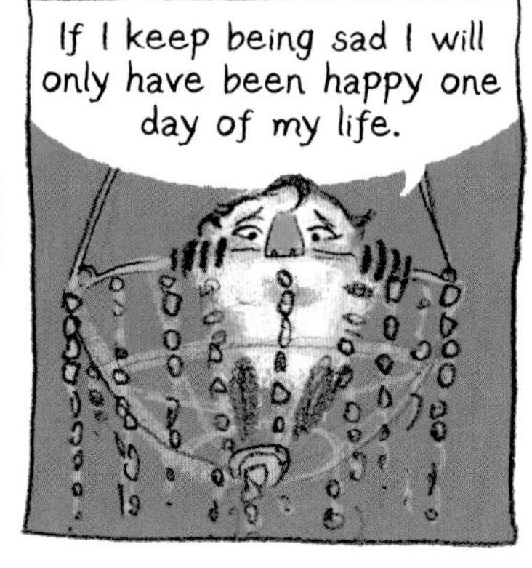
If I keep being sad I will only have been happy one day of my life.

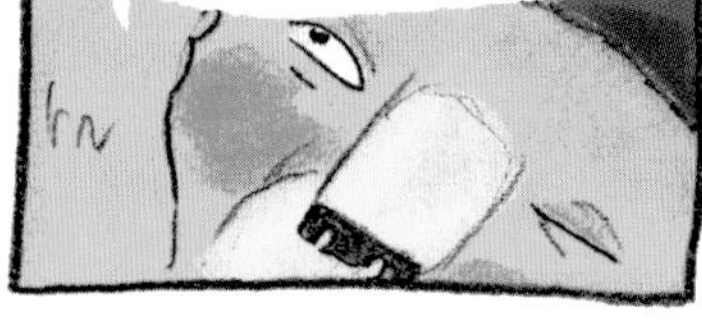
Not necessarily. Yesterday was only sad in the afternoon. So you've had one and a half happy days out of two. At that rate, you'll be mostly happy.

True. You know more than me.

What's it like to be older?

From what I can tell, it's mostly terrifying. So far I've been frightened every day of my life.

Cor.

RRUMBLE

We've arrived somewhere...
I'll get the letter!

Bonifacius? We need your help upstairs.
Oh ... OK.

This is my writing quill. I have used it for a long time, and now...
Uh, no, I don't want it!

What? No, no. I'm not giving it to you.
Oh.

It is infused with my knowledge. We will raise it, so that it may be my apprentice.

There must be three of us to do the ritual. You will be the third.
But I can't do ... um ... I don't even know what!
Just do as we do.

Baa.
Baa.

Baa.
Baa.
Baa?

Baa.
Baa.

BECOME!

It is done. I suppose.

Her name is Sophia. Take her downstairs.

Thank you for your help.
Hey, you made a new friend! Pleased?

I did it wrong, didn't I?

Oh, she looks happy though. Let's have some tea.

Sigh.
Wow! What's THAT?
Sophia. She's the new team member. Say hello!

Hello, Sophia!

HELLO

Yay! Hello!

So ... usually there's a letter?
WIPE
WIPE

Indeed ... it's just a standard N.I.P. You can handle that.

Off you go!
A standard what?

HA HA
HA
HA
HA
HAHAHA
HA

HA HA HAHA HA HAHAH
Sounds like they're having fun...
I know this smell. This is ... this is school.

HA HA HA HA
HA HA
The child is in here...
So what's a N.I.P.?

HAHA HA HA
"Naked in Public".
HA
HAHA
HA HA HA
HAHA
HA HA
HA HA
HA
HA

This is awful! Poor little guy!

What's going on here!

Wassili has no clothes on, Mister Bear, sir.

So? What's so funny about that?

I don't have clothes on either.
No.

What are you teaching these children? Don't they even know that they all look like that under their clothes?

I AM NAKƏD TOO.

You must be a very bad teacher.

That's it! Get out! And don't come back until you have some clothes on! I refuse to talk to ... weird naked animals!

What's weird about naked animals?
Nothing. These people are silly.
Hey! We're back! We need some clothes!
I thought you might.

Cool!

Does my bum look big in this?
Yay!
Yup.

Ta-daaaah! THIS is my outfit!
Woo hoo!

Wow! You think your teacher will like that?
I don't care! It flies!
Go show 'em!

SUPERWELLDONE!
That was EASY!
ZOOM

Well ... if everything is in order now, it's my time to go.

Sophia, you are in charge of the library now. You know all I ever wrote, and I wrote all I ever knew.

I trust you will do your work well.

CLICK
GOODBYE

STOP LEAVING US!

I DON'T WANT ANYONE TO LEAVE ANY MORE!
You're not leaving, right?

Noo. Don't worry. Not until you're ready to take over the house.
That'll be a while yet, then.
Where does that door go anyway?

Out of dreams. Everyone has to wake up some time. We have been dreaming for a long time...

Would you like a cup of tea?
Always!

DUM DEE DOO... Mm...

The dressing up was good though, wasn't it?
Yes, the dressing up was very good.

HOW TO MAKE BANANA MILKSHAKE

TO GET YOU THROUGH TOUGH TIMES

To Protect and To Instruct
DO NOT LOSE

Good morning! Here's your tea.
INK

Good morning!

Here's the letter.
IN
Well, let's see what's the matter, then!

INK

...so, it's: find the child, and help. Anything else?
Slurp

Hm?
Anything else?

Nothing.
Great! Let's go!

It's dark out here.
We'd better take a torch!

WELCOME

Turn on the torch, then.
CLICK
Um ... it is on.
Is it broken?
No, it's just ... not lighting anything.
OK. Let's go back to the house.
Yes.
OK.
Um ... Bonno?
Yes?
Are you sure this is the way back home?
No. I was following you.
WHAT? I was following YOU!
Oh no. HELP.
HELP. WE ARE LOST.
Don't tell everyone!
So, what do we do now??
SCRIBBLE SCRIBBLE
We can't read in the dark, Sophia.

We're doomed!
Stop shouting! Please! Be quiet!
All right. Who said that?
Please be quiet. It'll hear you.
It's the child! We found you!
Found me? Who are you?
We are your rescue team!
But you are lost, too!
I told you don't tell everyone.
ZAP!
Yikes!
Why are we glowing?
Dream energy.
What's that mean?
It means...
It's coming! You made it come here!

What's coming?
Ssshhh...

SHHHSHHSSSSS

AAAAAAAAH!
HHHHSSSSSHHHH

HSSSSSSSHHHHH

HSSSS
SSS

HHH
HHH

HSS
SSHHHS
This way! This way!

SSSS
SHHHSSSSSHSHSSSS
But...
Towards the light!
Leave it to me.

Hurry!

Stop fooling around. Come on. Where are you?

Show yourself!
You don't frighten me!

We can't leave her behind!
We have to.

CLUNK

RUMBLE
What is this place? It's moving.
rRUMBLE

I hope she's OK...
RUMBLE
Of course.
RUMBLE
RUMBLE

It's stopped.

What's out there?

That's our garage!

Thank you, turtle.

Are we safe now?
Yes. Yes, we are safe.

You can go home now. Through that door. Then you'll wake up.

And if you dream of darkness again ... um ... I ... I don't know.
It's OK. Thanks for saving me.

Don't worry.

She'll be back.

CLICK

Hello, guys.

What happened to your arm?
Ah? Oh. I must have lost it.

Fancy that... Oh no!

I was holding the sword on that side! Bother.

I shouldn't have brought the sword. It's yours.

Did you kill the darkness?
Of course not.

I'm sorry we messed up.

You didn't. You saved the child.
But you are hurt, and we didn't even make the nightmare go away...

Some dreams are scary every time. There is nothing you can do — except wake up.

Now you know everything. Oof.

Where are you going? You need some rest, sit down...
I do. I need some rest. I would have liked to stick around a bit longer to see what you get up to.
I like you. We chose well.

Sorry I lost your sword, Bonno.

Can you hear that? I think it's a cat. It sounds happy. There are happy things out there. Good.
There's nothing! You are imagining it.

No, no. Time to wake up! Have a good time. Goodbye!
GOODBYE

GOODBYE

I had a bad dream...

Buddy? What would happen to me if I went through that door?

You would wake up, and be a blanket again.

You can all leave if you want.

Where is Amali?
She's preserved herself. Behind the pickles.

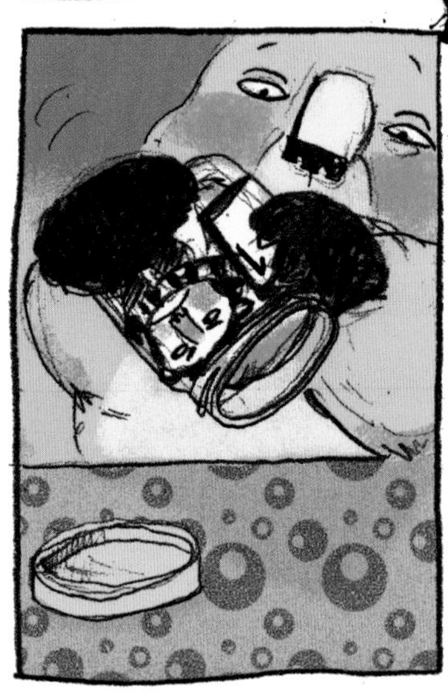

Should I get a spoon?
No.

Was the jam nice?
Yes, the jam was very nice.

Would you like to come out for breakfast?
No, I had jam.

We've been talking.
I see that.
It's all wrong.

HELP ME

WE NEED THE SWORD OF RIN

And if we don't have the sword? What else can we do?

NOTHING

All. Right. Then.

I'm ready! Let's go!

What? We lost the Sword of Rin, which we NEED, and so we'll take the mask of ... of what, of you? How is that supposed to help!?

It makes me feel better. Ready?
Yeah!

FOOMPH

I can't work like this!
Are you coming?

No sword! No instructions! Just a horrible drawing!

JAM

Wait!
You ...

ZAP!
ZAP!
ZAP!

... you don't know the way.

This is strange. She should be ... right here ...

... in this tree.

She IS the tree.

Now what? Should we try and pull her out or something?

Dance?
DANCE

Oh ... oh I know I know I know!

Like this ... around the tree!
Eh?

Hop. Hey...
Huh?

La?
La ... la ... hum...

Zip zap!

We did it!
Hurrah!

Is he ... is he gone?
Who?

Everything's OK now. Let's go home!
TEEHEE

Amali! Is this the way? Hey!
YAY DEE DAY

I said, is this...
DOO DEE DAAA

LAA LALAA

SHUT UP! BE QUIET!

Eeeeeeeek!

I TOLD YOU TO BE QUIET!

Don't cry...
He's the one who needs to shut up...

SILENCE!

Oh ... what are we supposed to do ... I don't know ... I ... can't...

I WILL SHUT YOU UP!

Well, I'm not scared ...

... any more ...

... than usual...

ROAR

SWOOP
SWIPE

SILENCE

Ack...

Oh no...
Save...
Help...
How...
How...

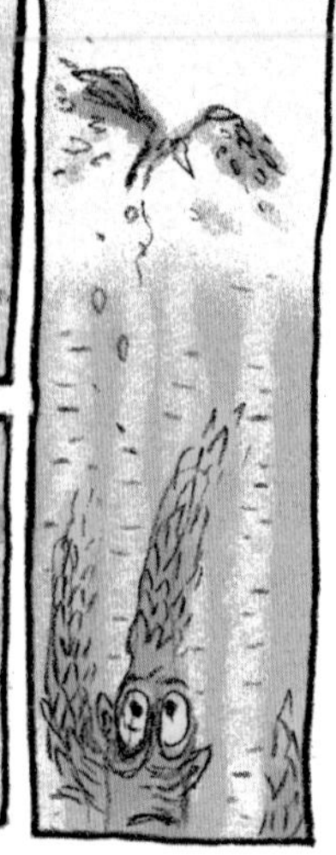

GO AMALI
TICKLE HERE
WHAT?!

Hee hee hee...

BAT
RAH!
BOINK

HEY!

STOP HURTING MY FRIENDS!
POP

TICKLE
TICKLE
TICKLE

BWA HA HA HA HA

HA HA HA
HA HA HA
HA

Shoo!
Shoo!
Go away!

Shoo!

We beat him! We did it! We knew how!
Awooooooo!

Thank you for saving me!
No problem.

They always do.

Goodbye!
Sweet dreams!

Hey, let's have breakfast again.

Can I have Chocolate Crunchies? With quadruple chocolate?
Well, as long as you can imagine what chocolate crunchies are like.

Yes.

Then you can.

I really fancy a cup of tea, myself.

Oh, hello! Do I know you?

I don't know why I came here. I'm not really into this old stuff...

I don't think they allow dogs in here.

Hi. It's busy here, is there a special exhibition or something?
Oh ... no I don't think so.

I just felt like coming here.
Me too.

Hey ... these are nice.

TOY RATTLES OR CONTAINERS -
USE UNKNOWN - EARLY DYNAST

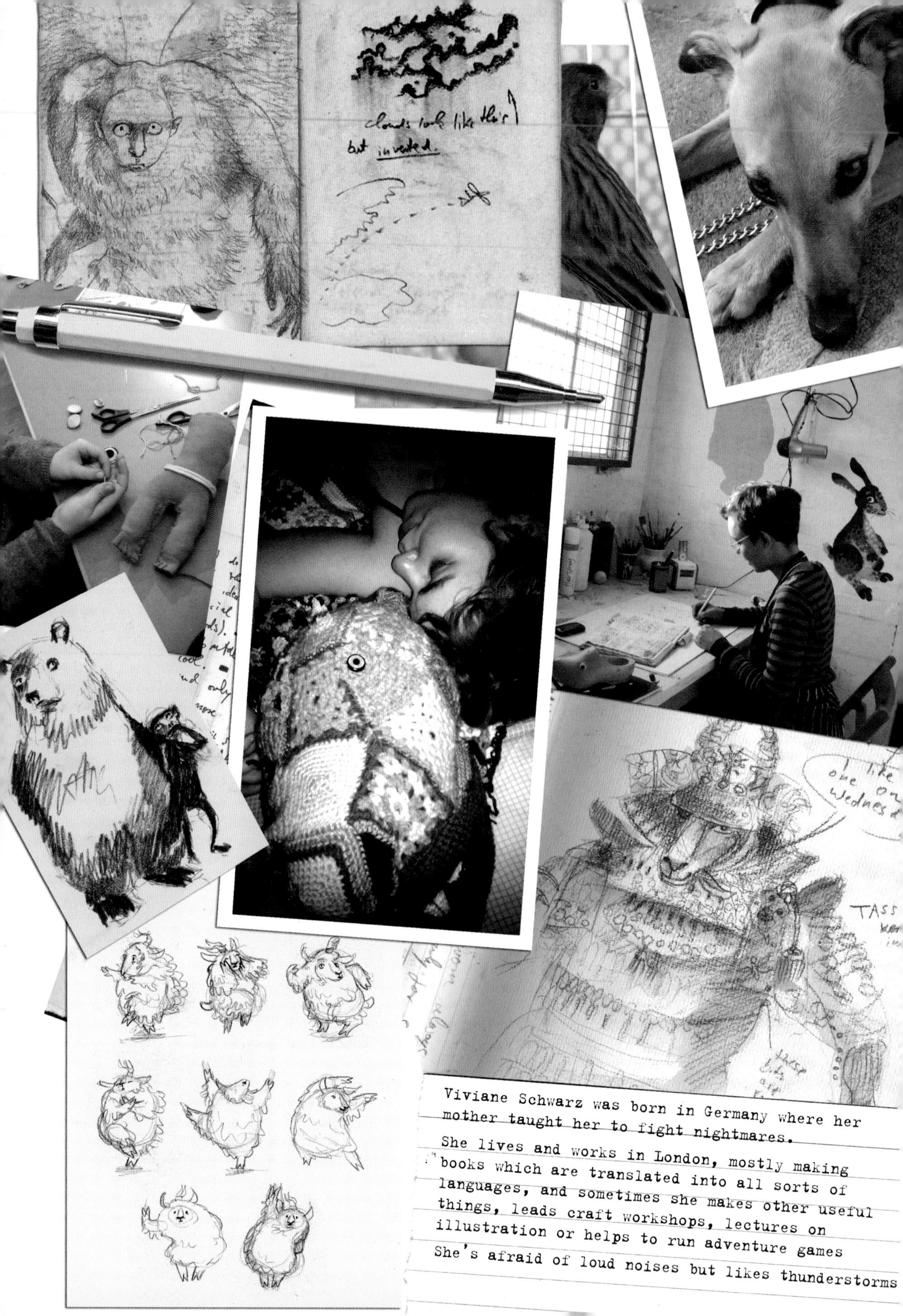

Viviane Schwarz was born in Germany where her mother taught her to fight nightmares.

She lives and works in London, mostly making books which are translated into all sorts of languages, and sometimes she makes other useful things, leads craft workshops, lectures on illustration or helps to run adventure games

She's afraid of loud noises but likes thunderstorms